# SENSATIONAL SPELLING GAMES

## TARGETING VOWEL SOUNDS TO IMPROVE STUDENT SPELLING

## CAROL DUFFY

**USER FRIENDLY RESOURCES**

**EDUCATIONAL PUBLISHERS**
www.userfr.com

Published by User Friendly Resources. Book No. 505

## TITLE
Book Name:      Sensational Spelling Games
Book Number:    505
ISBN 13:       978-1-86968-318-4
Published:      2007

## AUTHOR
Carol Duffy

## ACKNOWLEDGEMENTS
Designer:      Glen Honeybone
Illustrator:      Glen Honeybone
Editor:       Blue Duck Media
Proofreader:     Ross McKerras

## PUBLISHER:
User Friendly Resources

**United Kingdom Office**
Premier House
11 Marlborough Place
Brighton
East Sussex BN1 1UB
Ph: 0845-450-7502
Fax: 0845-688-0199

**New Zealand Office**
PO Box 1820
Christchurch
Ph: 0508-500-393
Fax: 0508-500-399

**Australian Office**
PO Box 914
Mascot, NSW 2020
Ph: 1800-553-890
Fax: 1800-553-891

**WEBSITE:** www.userfr.com
**E-MAIL:** info@userfr.com

**User Friendly Resources** specialises in publishing educational resources for teachers and students across a wide range of curriculum areas, at early childhood, primary and secondary levels. If you wish to know more about our resources, or if you think your resource ideas have publishing potential, please contact us at one of the above addresses.

All teachers are aware of the difficulties the English language presents to children learning to spell. One of the more difficult areas is that of vowel sounds. There are often several ways of spelling the same sound, a fact which children find confusing.

The games in this book present the most common spellings for the long vowel sounds and the vowel digraphs. Most of these games can be played in two ways: firstly with children reading the words and so becoming familiar with the various spelling when seen, and then with children writing the words and so practising the spellings themselves.

Instructions for playing both ways are given for each game. It is important to ensure the children are using the correct sound for the game they are playing. Some spellings have different sounds, but teachers should not allow a different sound for the purpose of these games.

I have tried out all the games in this book and they work. I hope they work for you and your pupils too.

 # Contents

## Preparation

Photocopy the game pages on coloured card. Laminate, if desired, and cut up the cards.

It is a good idea to glue the 'e' markers on to plastic counters. They will last longer as children tend to get a bit rough as they capture their opponent's words!

## How to play

1. Each player has a game card (bingo card) and 3 'e' counters. The word cards are placed face down on the table or in a container.

2. Players take turns to pick up a word card and place it over a matching picture on their game card. If the word does not match a picture on the player's card it is returned to the pile/ container.

3. If a player picks up a short vowel word, and wants to match it to a long-vowel picture on their game card, they may do so by adding an 'e' counter. E.g. pin + e → pine.

4. A player may capture another player's short-vowel word in this way, shouting "Mine!", taking the word, and putting it on his or her long-vowel picture with their 'e' counter. This must be done before their next turn. Words that already have a final 'e' cannot be captured.

5. The first player to match words to all the pictures on his or her card is the winner.

Note: Each bingo card has 3 short vowel pictures and 3 long vowel pictures that require a silent 'e'. The word cards are only short vowel words, the 'e' tokens are needed to make the long vowel words. Help students identify the pairs of words (eg. pin/pine, tub/tube). Each player needs to identify what words he/she will need to add the 'e's to to make his/her long vowel words (the right hand column in Set One and left in Set Two of the game card).

**Mine!**

| | | | |
|---|---|---|---|
| kit | kit | rip | rip |
| plan | plan | rag | rag |
| strip | strip | bit | bit |
| cap | cap | sit | sit |
| fin | fin | hug | hug |
| rod | rod | plum | plum |

| spin | spin | rob | rob |
| man | man | cub | cub |
| cut | cut | pan | pan |
| pin | pin | pip | pip |
| can | can | tap | tap |
| tub | tub | win | win |

# Mine!

Sensational Spelling Games

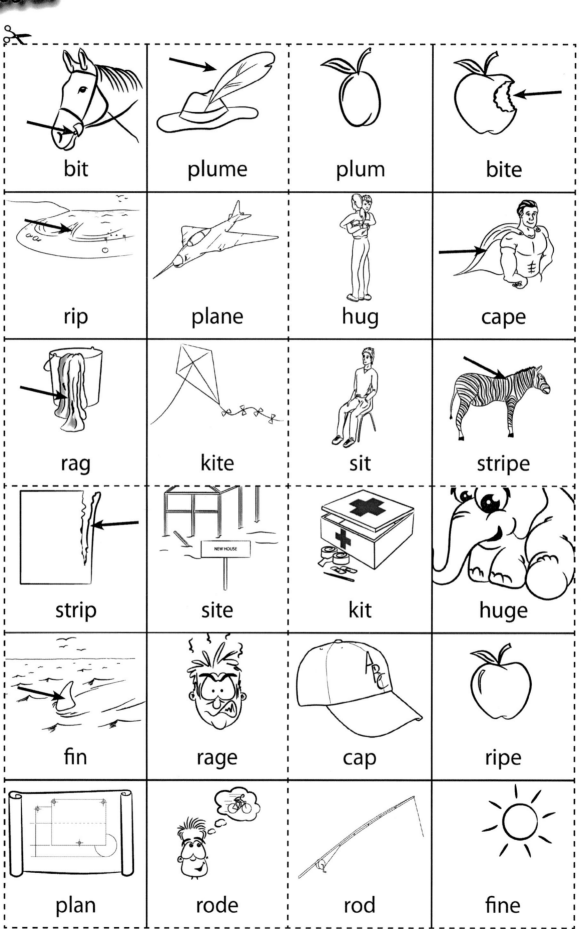

| | | | |
|---|---|---|---|
| bit | plume | plum | bite |
| rip | plane | hug | cape |
| rag | kite | sit | stripe |
| strip | site | kit | huge |
| fin | rage | cap | ripe |
| plan | rode | rod | fine |

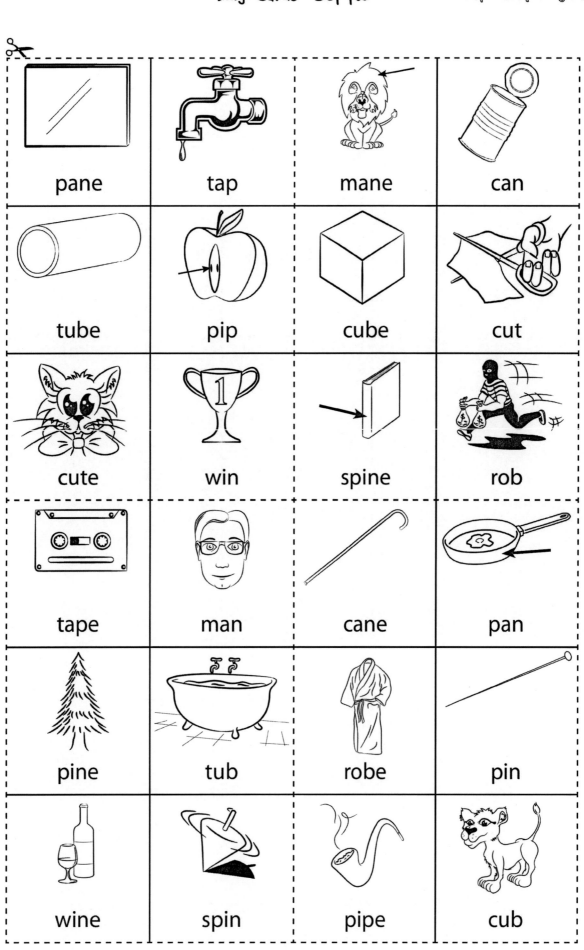

| | | | |
|---|---|---|---|
| pane | tap | mane | can |
| tube | pip | cube | cut |
| cute | win | spine | rob |
| tape | man | cane | pan |
| pine | tub | robe | pin |
| wine | spin | pipe | cub |

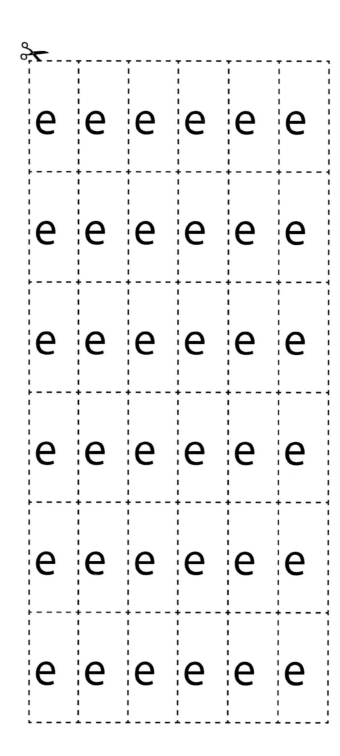

## Preparation

Photocopy all three pages (12-14). (Copy beginning and end cards on different colours to avoid muddling and much sorting.)

Make up sail boat markers.

## How to play

**1.** Players place boats ready to 'Sail Away.'

**2.** Deal 3 beginning cards and 3 ending cards to each player. Place the rest face down in two piles in the centre of the table.

**3.** The first player makes as many words as he can with his 6 cards, a card may only be used in one word. (If an ending card is a word on its own it may be used as such (as 'ape' or 'ale' in the example below)). That player then moves the number of squares on the board equal to the number of cards he has used. Words must have a long 'A' sound.

E.g. A player has:

| br | d | st |
|----|---|----|

| ale | ape | ain |
|-----|-----|-----|

He makes:

| br | ain |
|----|-----|

| st | ale |
|----|-----|

(Brain, stale)

Ape is a word, so he has used 5 cards and moves 5 squares. Ale is not counted because they have used it in 'stale'.

**Strategy Tip:** He may choose to use only 2 cards (making just one word) and so catch the wind (see square 2). However, if words can be made, they cannot 'pass'. It is not an option to make no words to avoid a hazard.

**4.** The turn ends by discarding <u>cards used</u> and picking up replacement cards from centre piles. You should always have 3 beginning and 3 ending cards.

**5.** If no words can be made, the player may discard one of each card and pick up replacements. This counts as their turn.

**6.** The first player to reach Safe Bay by exact count is the winner. (Remember the strategy tip mentioned above.)

**7.** If all cards are used before a player reaches Safe Bay, shuffle and replace piles in the centre.

| 64 ⚓ SAFE BAY | 63 | 62 *Whale in the way. Detour* | 61 | 60 | 59 | 58 *Pirates Retreat* ☠ | 57 |
|---|---|---|---|---|---|---|---|
| 49 | 50 | 51 | 52 *Hurricane blows you about* | 53 | 54 | 55 | 56 |
| 48 | 47 | 46 | 45 | 44 | 43 | 42 | 41 *Good wind blows you forward* |
| 33 | 34 | 35 | 36 | 37 | 38 *Strong currents push you forward* | 39 | 40 |
| 32 | 31 *Big wave pushes you back* | 30 | 29 | 28 | 27 | 26 | 25 |
| 17 | 18 | 19 | 20 *Good wind blows you forward* | 21 | 22 | 23 | 24 |
| 16 | 15 | 14 | 13 | 12 | 11 | 10 *Good wind blows you forward* | 9 |
| 1 *Sail Away* | 2 *Good wind blows you forward* | 3 | 4 | 5 | 6 *Strong currents push you forward* | 7 | 8 |

✂

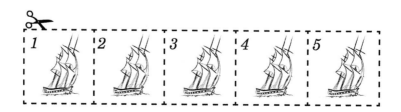

1  2  3  4  5

| | | | | |
|---|---|---|---|---|
| b | br | c | cr | d |
| dr | f | fr | w | g |
| gr | h | l | m | n |
| p | pr | pl | qu | r |
| s | st | sp | sh | sl |
| t | tr | t | tr | s |
| b | br | c | cr | d |
| dr | f | fr | w | g |
| gr | h | l | m | n |
| p | pr | pl | qu | r |
| s | st | sp | sh | sl |

Sensational Spelling Games

| | | | | |
|---|---|---|---|---|
| ain | ain | ay | ay | ay |
| ay | ake | ake | ail | ail |
| ale | ale | ait | aint | ey |
| aid | ade | age | ace | ate |
| ate | ame | ame | ave | ave |
| ape | eigh | ape | eigh | ate |
| ain | ain | ay | ay | ay |
| ay | ake | ake | ail | ail |
| ale | ale | ait | aint | ey |
| aid | ade | age | ace | ate |
| ate | ame | ame | ave | ave |

These are some of the words you can make while 'Sailing Away.' Can you make any others?

| | | | | | |
|---|---|---|---|---|---|
| brain | bay | bake | bait | bale | aid |
| drain | bray | brake | gait | dale | braid |
| fain | cray | cake | trait | gale | laid |
| gain | day | drake | wait | male | maid |
| grain | dray | fake | await | pale | paid |
| lain | fray | lake | | sale | plaid |
| main | gay | make | | stale | raid |
| pain | hay | quake | ate | tale | staid |
| plain | lay | rake | bate | wale | |
| rain | may | sake | crate | | |
| stain | pay | stake | date | | bade |
| Spain | pray | slake | fate | | fade |
| slain | play | take | grate | bail | wade |
| train | ray | wake | | fail | made |
| wain | say | | hate | frail | spade |
| | stay | | late | Gail | shade |
| bane | spay | page | mate | hail | trade |
| cane | slay | rage | plate | mail | |
| crane | tray | sage | rate | nail | |
| Dane | way | stage | state | pail | |
| mane | | | slate | quail | cape |
| pane | fey | brave | spate | rail | drape |
| plane | grey | crave | | sail | gape |
| sane | prey | Dave | ace | tail | grape |
| | trey | gave | brace | trail | nape |
| | | grave | face | wail | rape |
| | | | grace | | shape |
| faint | weigh | pave | lace | came | tape |
| paint | neigh | rave | mace | dame | |
| quaint | sleigh | save | pace | fame | |
| saint | | stave | place | frame | |
| taint | | slave | space | game | |
| | | shave | trace | lame | |
| | | wave | | name | |
| | | | | same | |
| | | | | shame | |
| | | | | tame | |

15

Long 'e' sound

2-4 Players

## Preparation

Photocopy cards on coloured card.
Laminate if desired.

## How to play 'Familee', for reading practice:

1.  Shuffle cards and deal 5 cards to each player. Put the rest in a pile, face down, on the table. Place any existing pairs face up on the table in front of you.

2.  The first player asks the player on their left if they have a particular card (e.g. "Do you have 'lady'?") or a card from a specific family (e.g. "Do you have a member of the 'y' says 'e' family?").

3.  If the answer is yes the card is given to the first player, who places the matching pair on the table, face up. If the player does not have it they answer: "Go Fish!" and the first player can then ask the other players. If no-one has the required card the first player picks a card from the pile and play passes to the next player.

4.  When a player has no cards in their hand, they pick one up from the pile at any time. The game ends when a player has no more cards left to match.

5.  The winner is the player with the most pairs at the end of the game.

## How to play 'Familee', for spelling practice:

1.  At the end of a game of "Go Fish!" each player in turn chooses one family he/she has collected.

2.  The player reads the words from the family for the other players to write.

3.  The players write the 4 words and the name of the family and 2 other words belonging to that family.

4.  Scoring:      5 points for all 4 words spelt correctly
                  5 points for identifying the family
                  5 points for 2 extra words spelt correctly

5.  When all players have dictated their families add up the total points to find the winner.

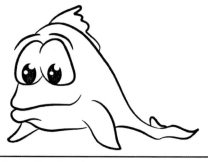

'ee' says 'E'

'ee' says 'E'

'ee' says 'E'

'ee' says 'E'

cheese
feet
sheep

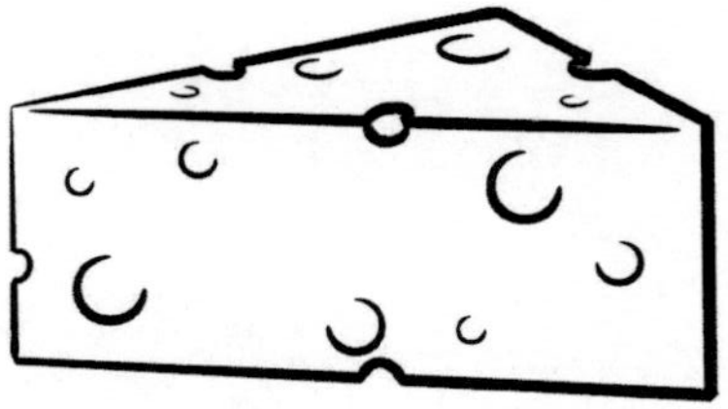

bee
feet
sheep

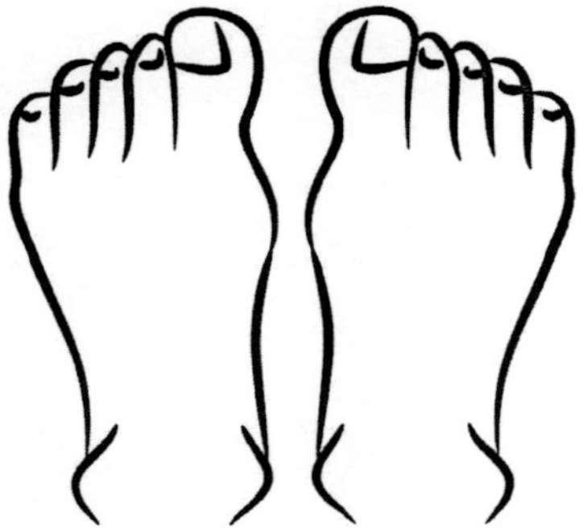

bee
cheese
sheep

bee
cheese
feet

'ie' says 'E'

'ie' says 'E'

'ie' says 'E'

'ie' says 'E'

shield
mischief
chief

piece
mischief
chief

piece
shield
chief

piece
shield
mischief

cookies
dont touch!

# Familee

| 'e_e' says 'E' | athlete<br>concrete<br>compete | 'y' says 'E' | baby<br>daisy<br>lady |
| --- | --- | --- | --- |
| 'e_e' says 'E' | athlete<br>compete<br>complete | 'y' says 'E' | baby<br>daisy<br>lazy |
| 'e_e' says 'E' | athlete<br>concrete<br>complete | 'y' says 'E' | baby<br>lady<br>lazy |
| 'e_e' says 'E' | compete<br>complete<br>concrete | 'y' says 'E' | lady<br>daisy<br>lazy |

Sensational Spelling Games

| | | | 'ey' says 'E' |
|---|---|---|---|
| beast<br>peas<br>teapot | | turkey<br>key<br>donkey | |

'ea' says 'E'

| | | | 'ey' says 'E' |
|---|---|---|---|
| beach<br>peas<br>teapot | | money<br>key<br>donkey | |

'ea' says 'E'

| | | | 'ey' says 'E' |
|---|---|---|---|
| beach<br>beast<br>teapot | | money<br>turkey<br>donkey | |

'ea' says 'E'

| | | | 'ey' says 'E' |
|---|---|---|---|
| beach<br>beast<br>peas | | money<br>turkey<br>key | |

'ea' says 'E'

Long 'i' sound

2-6 Players

## Preparation

Photocopy target on strong card, cover with clear seal.
Photocopy enough individual cards for players.
Have a supply of large and small counters.

## Each player needs:

**1.** One large and one small counter.

**2.** An individual card and pencil/pen .

## How to play :

**1.** Set the winning target:
- Most words in the time limit
- *or* first player to fill their card
- *or* first player to have 3 words in each column.

**2.** Take turns to 'tiddlywink' the small counter onto the target (game board) using the large counter.

**3.** Player writes a word in the column of the individual card that corresponds with the area of the target on which the counter came to rest. (e.g. stops on 'ie', player could write 'pie' in the 'ie' column.)

**4.** If a counter lands halfway between two targets, the player may choose which to use.

**5.** The winner is the first to achieve the desired goal.

## Game Board

Sensational Spelling Games

Cut around the outside edge and the small marked lines.
Fold up the outer edge on the dotted line and glue the corners to make a low rim around the target.

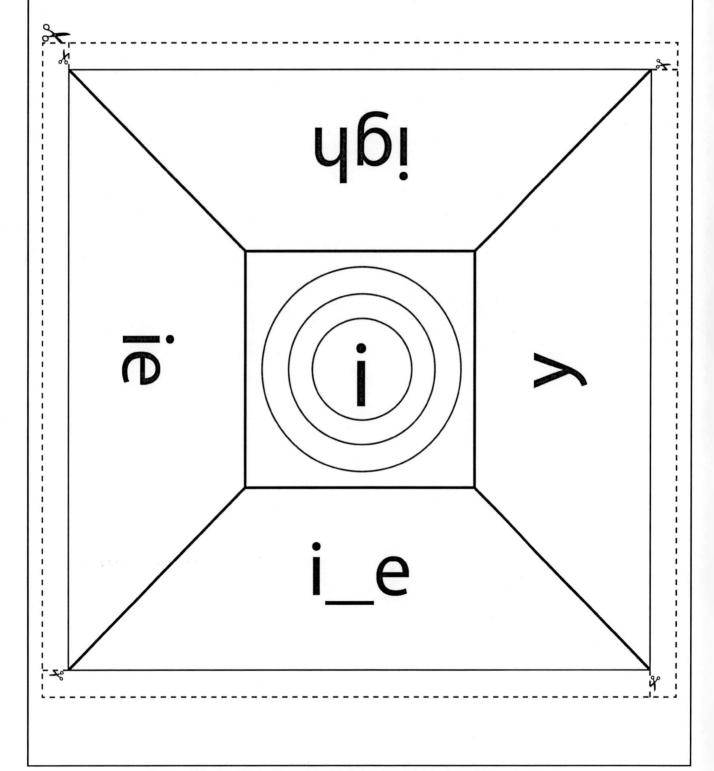

## Score cards

| i | i_e | ie | y | igh |
|---|-----|----|----|-----|
|   |     |    |   |     |
|   |     |    |   |     |
|   |     |    |   |     |
|   |     |    |   |     |
|   |     |    |   |     |

| i | i_e | ie | y | igh |
|---|-----|----|----|-----|
|   |     |    |   |     |
|   |     |    |   |     |
|   |     |    |   |     |
|   |     |    |   |     |
|   |     |    |   |     |

| i | i_e | ie | y | igh |
|---|-----|----|----|-----|
|   |     |    |   |     |
|   |     |    |   |     |
|   |     |    |   |     |
|   |     |    |   |     |
|   |     |    |   |     |

# Oh, Go Home!

Long 'o' sound

2-4 Players

## Preparation

Photocopy board.

Make up die and counters. Colour each set of counters a different colour.

You also need a normal 6-sided die.

## How to play (reading only):

1.  Each player places their four counters on the four corners of the board.

2.  The first player throws both dice and moves the counter with the spelling indicated by the letter die the number of spaces indicated by the normal die. (So if a player throws a 3 and 'oa' they count 3 'oa' words from where the 'oa' counter is and place their counter on the third of those words. The child must read each word as they move. If they are unable to read a word they must stop on the last one they could read. This means that if a 6 is thrown and the child can only read 2 words, they only move 2 spaces.)

3.  If a player lands on another player's counter it becomes captured and must be returned to the corner and start its journey again.

4.  The winner is the first player to get all four counters home.

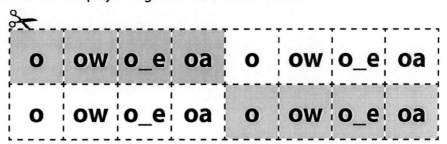

| o | ow | o_e | oa | o | ow | o_e | oa |
|---|----|-----|----|---|----|-----|----|
| o | ow | o_e | oa | o | ow | o_e | oa |

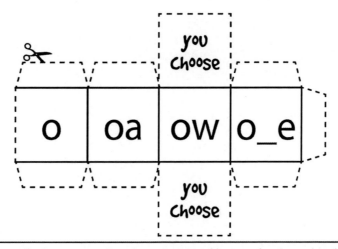

you Choose

| o | oa | ow | o_e |
|---|----|----|-----|

you Choose

| ow | tow | grow | blow | mow | throw | show | slow | flow | o_e |
|---|---|---|---|---|---|---|---|---|---|
| groan | foam | load | road | toad | foal | goal | coal | glow | note |
| moan | Dodo | poncho | Mexico | obtain | potato | tomato | toast | know | wrote |
| stoat | bravo | footnote | compose | arose | trombone | volcano | roast | row | robe |
| throat | banjo | quote | tomorrow | | | Tokyo | soap | window | rode |
| moat | okay | alcove | shallow | HoME | | buffalo | hoax | pillow | code |
| goat | ogre | pole | narrow | lifeboat | petticoat | oath | coax | yellow | hope |
| coat | open | hole | below | elbow | crow | snow | follow | fellow | mope |
| boat | over | joke | poke | stoke | hose | rose | nose | zone | slope |
| oa | hello | oval | so | ho | oh | lo | go | no | o |

# Supermarket Queue

Long 'u' sound

2-5 Players

## Preparation

Photocopy all four pages onto card.

Colour the game tokens.

Cut out product cards, game tokens and shopping lists.

You need a normal 1-6 die.

## How to play (for reading practice):

1. Shuffle product cards and place, **face up**, on supermarket shelves (game board).

2. Give each player a game token and a shopping list containing a list of products.

3. Players move around the supermarket according to the number thrown on the die. A player may take a product off a shelf on either side of the aisle when they land on a square adjacent to a product on their list. If a throw takes a player past a product on his list he may go back on his next throw. A player may not change direction within a turn.

4. The winner is the first player to obtain all the products on his list and leave the supermarket via the checkout.

## How to play (for spelling practice):

1. Shuffle product cards and place, **face down**, on supermarket shelves.

2. Give each player a game token and a shopping list, for the spelling game.

3. Players move around the supermarket according to the number thrown on the die. The player takes a product off a shelf on either side of the aisle, turns over the card and reads it to the next player, who writes the '**u**' word in the correct space on their shopping list. (Example: Player 1 reads "tin of cat **food**, spell food". Player 2 writes 'food' in the 'oo' space on their card.)

4. Player 2 gives the card to player 1 to check the spelling – if it is correct (and in the correct space) they leave it but if it is incorrect they rub it out.

5. Play continues until one player leaves the supermarket. The player with the most words on their shopping list at that time is the winner.

Note: • Play is only in one direction in this game.
      • If players land on a square with no products left on the shelf they throw again.

# Supermarket Queue

Move on white squares, place 'products' on 'shelves' (shaded squares).

CHECK OUT

ENTRY

# Supermarket Queue

## Product cards

✂

| | | | | | |
|---|---|---|---|---|---|
| tin of st<u>ew</u> | honeyd<u>ew</u> melon | ch<u>ew</u>ing gum | n<u>ew</u> potatoes | cash<u>ew</u> nuts | gl<u>ue</u> stick |
| bl<u>ue</u>berries | m<u>ue</u>sli | barbec<u>ue</u> sauce | box of tiss<u>ue</u>s | tin of fr<u>ui</u>t salad | litre of orange j<u>ui</u>ce |
| fr<u>ui</u>ty yoghurt | two grapefr<u>ui</u>t | bottle of fr<u>ui</u>t juice | b<u>oo</u>t laces | tin of beetr<u>oo</u>t | tin of cat f<u>oo</u>d |
| two sc<u>oo</u>ps of ice cream | set of measuring sp<u>oo</u>ns | bag of pr<u>une</u>s | t<u>ube</u> of toothpaste | ball of j<u>ute</u> | 30cm r<u>ule</u>r |
| ice c<u>ube</u> tray | tin of t<u>u</u>na | a c<u>u</u>cumber | a calc<u>u</u>lator | moist<u>u</u>rising lotion | book about <u>u</u>nicorns |

✂

Game Tokens

## Shopping Lists
(for reading game)

| Shopping List | Shopping List | Shopping List | Shopping List | Shopping List |
|---|---|---|---|---|
| tin of st<u>ew</u> | honey<u>dew</u> melon | chewing gum | n<u>ew</u> potatoes | cash<u>ew</u> nuts |
| gl<u>ue</u> stick | bl<u>ue</u>berries | m<u>ue</u>sli | barbeq<u>ue</u> sauce | box of tiss<u>ue</u>s |
| tin of fr<u>ui</u>t salad | litre of orange j<u>ui</u>ce | fr<u>ui</u>ty yoghurt | two grapefr<u>ui</u>t | bottle of fr<u>ui</u>t juice |
| b<u>oo</u>t laces | tin of beetr<u>oo</u>t | tin of cat f<u>oo</u>d | two sc<u>oo</u>ps of ice cream | set of measuring sp<u>oo</u>ns |
| bag of pr<u>u</u>nes | t<u>u</u>be of toothpaste | ball of j<u>u</u>te | 30cm r<u>u</u>ler | ice c<u>u</u>be tray |
| tin of t<u>u</u>na | a c<u>u</u>cumber | a calculator | moist<u>u</u>rising lotion | book about <u>u</u>nicorns |

| Shopping List | | ew | ue | ui | oo | u_e | u |
| --- | --- | --- | --- | --- | --- | --- | --- |
| Shopping List | | ew | ue | ui | oo | u_e | u |
| Shopping List | | ew | ue | ui | oo | u_e | u |
| Shopping List | | ew | ue | ui | oo | u_e | u |
| Shopping List | | ew | ue | ui | oo | u_e | u |

# oR Rummy

## Preparation

Photocopy cards and cut out.

## How to play (for reading practice):

1.  Deal 5 cards to each player.

2.  The first player puts out any set of 3 or more <u>rhyming</u> words (some rhyming words are spelt differently, e.g. cause, gauze). Player then picks up cards from the pile to have five in his or her hand at all times.

3.  If a player can't make a rhyme, he or she picks up 1 card from the pile and discards 1.

4.  Score 5 points for every set of 3 plus one bonus for every extra card in a set.
    (Wild card – the clown – can be used for any card.)

5.  Winner is the player with the most points.

## How to play (for spelling practice):

1.  Play as above.

2.  At the end of the game, each player shuffles his or her sets and, in turn, dictates the words to the other players.

3.  Score one point for every word spelt correctly.

 **Word Cards**

| ball | fall | stall | mall | tall |
|------|------|-------|------|------|

| clause | talk | stalk | walk | chalk |
|--------|------|-------|------|-------|

| tore | store | sore | core | score |
|------|-------|------|------|-------|

| fort | port | sort | sport | short |
|------|------|------|-------|-------|

| saw | straw | raw | flaw | jaw |
| lawn | fawn | dawn | yawn | pawn |
| haunt | jaunt | daunt | gaunt | taunt |
| cause | gauze | pause | | |

## Preparation

Copy, cut up and laminate game board and cards.
5 coloured counters per player

'ar' & 'as' sounds

2-4 Players

## How to play (for reading practice):

1.  Shuffle word cards and place face down in centre of track. Place pile of counters in centre as well.

2.  Players place cars on start line.

3.  In turn pick up top card, read, and if correct move to next word that contains the letter sound. Return card to bottom of pile.

4.  If a square is occupied, players may pass others to the next unoccupied square with the matching letter sound.

5.  First player to complete 5 laps (or agreed number) wins.

## How to play (for spelling practice):

Play as above but the previous player picks up the card and dictates the word.

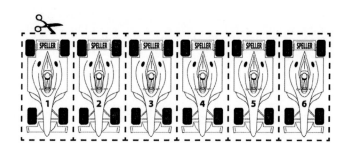

**Word Cards**

| | | | | |
|---|---|---|---|---|
| car | star | far | jar | class |
| pass | glass | brass | mask | task |
| flask | cask | last | fast | past |
| mast | cart | chart | dart | part |
| hard | yard | card | guard | |

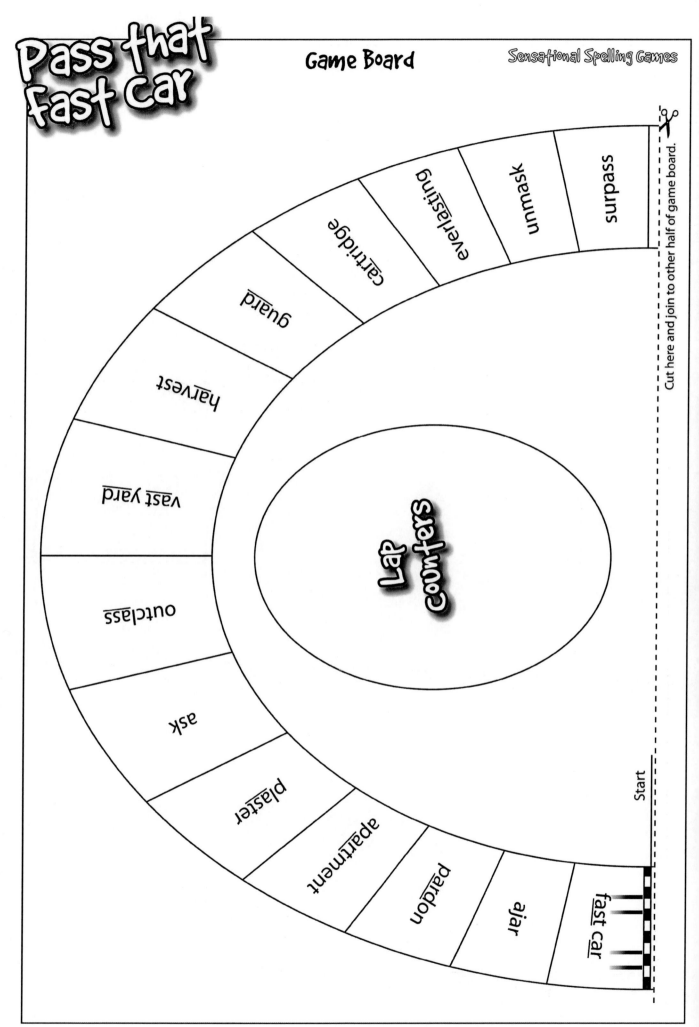

Cut here and join to other half of game board.

surpass

unmask

everlasting

cartridge

guard

harvest

vast yard

outclass

Lap Counters

ask

plaster

apartment

pardon

ajar

fast car

Start

# Game Board

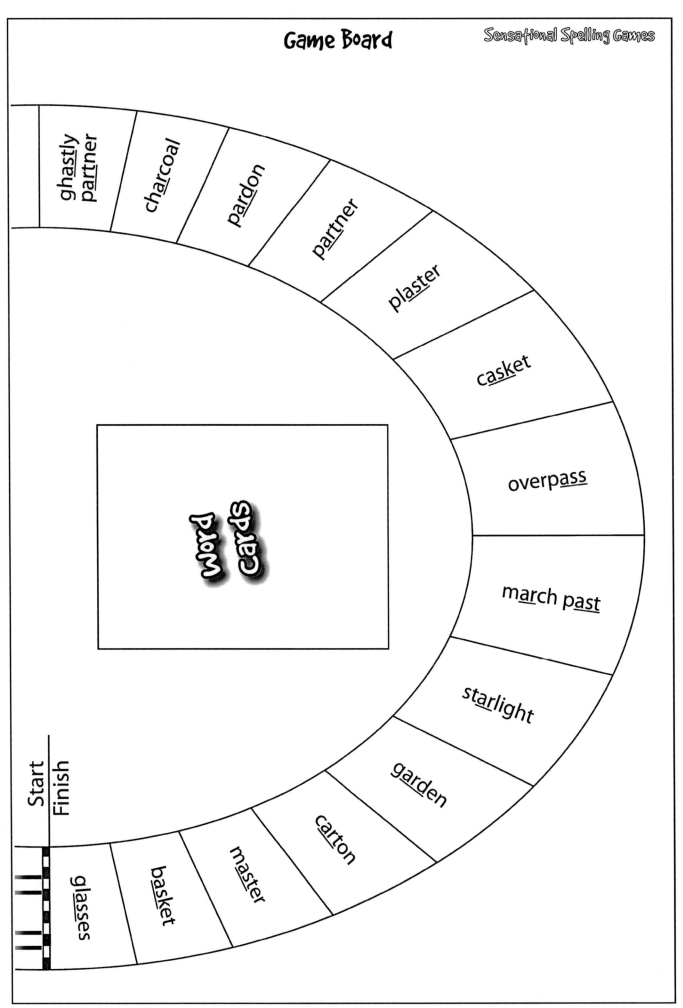

ghastly par<u>t</u>ner

charcoal

par<u>d</u>on

par<u>t</u>ner

pla<u>st</u>er

ca<u>sk</u>et

overpa<u>ss</u>

m<u>ar</u>ch p<u>ast</u>

st<u>ar</u>light

g<u>ar</u>den

c<u>ar</u>ton

m<u>a</u>ster

b<u>a</u>sket

g<u>la</u>sses

Word Cards

Start
Fin<u>i</u>sh

# Clown House

## Preparation

Copy, laminate, cut out house parts and word cards as required for the number of students playing.

You need a normal 1-6 die.

## How to play (for reading practice):

1. Place the pile of word cards face down in the centre of the table. Also place the house parts on table in piles according to type.

2. Students take turns throwing the die, picking up a card and reading all the words on it. If read correctly students return the card to the bottom of the pile and take the house part as indicated by the die. If the part indicated is not needed (they have it already or cannot yet use it) then no move is made.

3. The winner is the first to complete their house.

4. Numbers indicate these parts:
   1. Walls – need 2
   2. Roof – need 2 halves
   3. Door
   4. Chimney
   5. Windows – need 5
   6. Throw again

5. Players must start with walls – after all you can't put doors and windows in if the walls aren't there! A chimney may not be taken until the roof is complete.

## How to play (for spelling practice):

Play as above but instead of taking card for oneself, the previous player takes the card and dictates the words to the player. If spelt correctly, the player gains the house part.

## Window cards for game board:

## Game Board

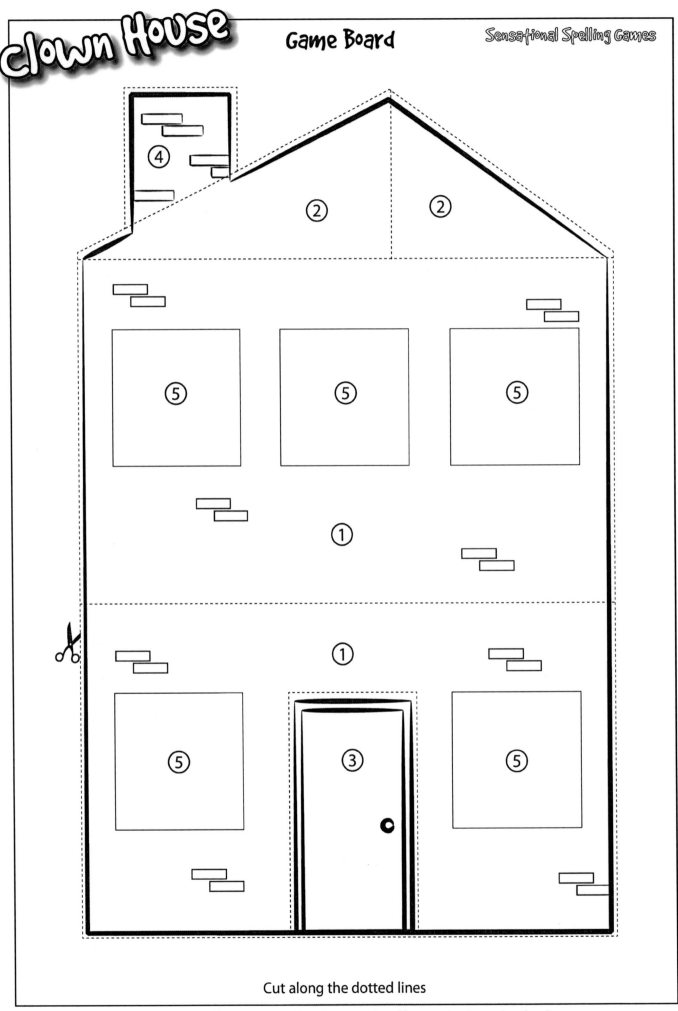

Cut along the dotted lines

| | | | |
|---|---|---|---|
| owl<br>fowl<br>howl<br>growl | our<br>hour<br>flour<br>sour | towel<br>vowel<br>dowel<br>trowel | ouch<br>couch<br>crouch<br>pouch |
| cow<br>bow<br>how<br>now | prowl<br>scowl<br>cowl<br>jowl | out<br>bout<br>lout<br>pout | mouth<br>mouthful<br>south<br>sou'wester |
| count<br>fountain<br>mount<br>mountain | house<br>mouse<br>spouse<br>louse | vow<br>row<br>wow<br>sow | tower<br>shower<br>power<br>flower |
| cower<br>bower<br>glower<br>flower | town<br>down<br>clown<br>frown | snout<br>scout<br>spout<br>sprout | round<br>ground<br>found<br>mound |

Sensational Spelling Games

| | | | |
|---|---|---|---|
| allow<br>disallow<br>avow<br>endow | powder<br>chowder<br>louder<br>prouder | loud<br>proud<br>cloud<br>shroud | frown<br>crown<br>brown<br>drown |
| ounce<br>pounce<br>bounce<br>flounce | outside<br>output<br>outlaw<br>outline | bow-wow<br>pow-wow<br>somehow<br>anyhow | flower<br>sunflower<br>wallflower<br>cauliflower |
| announce<br>denounce<br>pronounce<br>renounce | eiderdown<br>downtown<br>down-and-out<br>down-to-earth | crown<br>overcrowd<br>powder<br>chowder | bough<br>plough<br>slough<br>drought |
| bloodhound<br>compound<br>spellbound<br>expound | noun<br>pronoun<br>mountain<br>account | background<br>foreground<br>underground<br>surround | lookout<br>throughout<br>without<br>doubt |

# Coins for Toys

'oi' & 'oy' sounds

2-8 Players

## Preparation

Photocopy game board page on coloured card.
Back word cards with coin pictures. Laminate if desired.
Cut up the cards long the dotted lines.
Sort cards according to pictures on back– keep these in piles.
Cut out counters and laminate if desired.

## How to play (for reading practice):

1. Each player needs a counter and matching toy card representing the toy they would like to win.

2. Place the cards in piles in the centre of the board, picture side up.

3. First player picks up a card matching the first picture on the board. If they can read the words correctly **they mark the value indicated on their toy card** and move that number.

4. If the player cannot read the words the card is put on the bottom of the pile and the player does not move.

5. Continue in this way until a player has £20 to buy a toy.

6. The winner is the first one to buy a toy.

7. Players may need to go around the board more than once.

## How to play (for spelling practice):

1. Play as above, but the teacher or another player picks up the cards for each player and dictates the words or sentence.

2. The player moves and marks the toy card if the spelling is correct.

3. The winner is the first one to buy a toy.

# Coins for Toys

Game Board

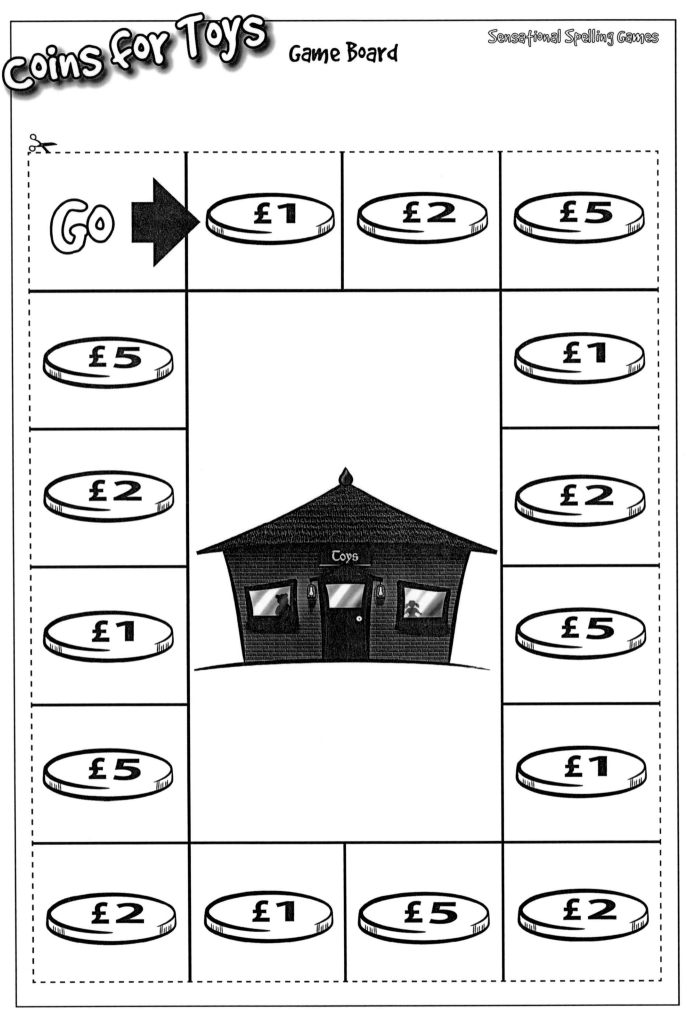

# Coins for Toys

Coins

Photocopy on to the reverse of page 44.

| £1 | £1 | £1 | £1 | £1 |
|----|----|----|----|----|
| £1 | £1 | £1 | £1 | £1 |
| £2 | £2 | £2 | £2 | £2 |
| £2 | £2 | £2 | £2 | £2 |
| £5 | £5 | £5 | £5 | £5 |
| £5 | £5 | £5 | £5 | £5 |
| £5 | £5 | £5 | £5 | £5 |

 **Word Cards**

Photocopy on to the reverse of page 43.

| | | | | |
|---|---|---|---|---|
| enjoy<br>enjoyment<br>enjoyable<br><br>£2 | boy<br>coy<br>joy<br>toy<br><br>£2 | voyage<br>oyster<br>convoy<br><br>£5 | annoy<br>annoying<br>annoyed<br><br>£2 | boy<br>Roy<br>Troy<br><br>£1 |
| destroy<br>deploy<br><br>£2 | employ<br>employer<br>employee<br>employment<br><br>£5 | joy<br>enjoy<br>annoy<br><br>£1 | royal<br>loyal<br>royalty<br>loyalty<br><br>£5 | joy<br>joyful<br>joyous<br><br>£2 |
| void<br>avoid<br>devoid<br><br>£5 | poise<br>poison<br><br>£5 | point<br>appoint<br>disappoint<br>appointment<br><br>£5 | oil<br>toil<br>toilet<br><br>£1 | voice<br>choice<br>rejoice<br><br>£2 |
| ointment<br>appointment<br><br>£2 | oil<br>foil<br>soil<br>spoil<br><br>£2 | noise<br>poise<br>hoist<br><br>£2 | oil<br>boil<br>coil<br>foil<br><br>£1 | coin<br>join<br>loin<br><br>£1 |
| Roy oiled the toy.<br><br>£1 | The boy rubbed ointment on his sore joint.<br><br>£2 | Troy spoiled the oysters by boiling them.<br><br>£5 | Troy enjoyed the voyage.<br><br>£2 | Point to the boiling oil.<br><br>£2 |
| A convoy of boats voyaged to the oil rig.<br><br>£5 | Avoid poisoning the soil.<br><br>£2 | Rejoice when your team scores a point.<br><br>£2 | Make a joyful noise.<br><br>£1 | Troy pointed out the oil leak.<br><br>£2 |
| Roy enjoys annoying Troy.<br><br>£1 | The employee kept his appointment with his employer.<br><br>£5 | Boys' voices can be noisy.<br><br>£1 | Employees should be loyal to their employers.<br><br>£5 | The poisonous plant grows in soil.<br><br>£2 |

# Coins for Toys

Toy cards

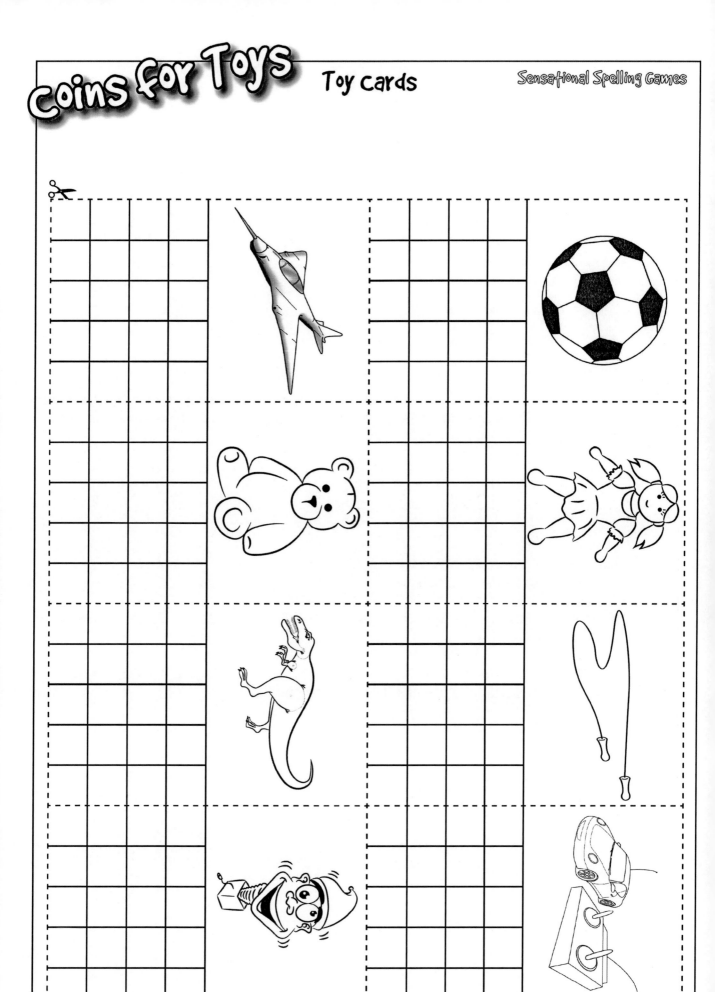

# Er, What's the Word?

## Preparation

Make up the 6 dice.

Players need a pencil and individual copies of the score card for writing words.

The teacher needs a copy of the word list.

## How to play :

1.  Players take turns throwing 6 dice and make as many words as possible from the letters thrown. Score 5 points for each word made. Score 5 bonus points for a 2-syllable word ending in 'er'.

2.  e.g. Throw:

    Make 'birth' (5 points), 'girth' (5 points) and 'burger' (5 + bonus 5 = 10 points).
    The total for this throw is 20 points.

3.  **Note: words must have 'er' sound.** Words such as 'bear' or 'beard' are not permissable as they have an 'air' sound.

4.  **Words must be on the word list.** But if a player can create a word not on the list, and verify it in the dictionary, it counts for 5 points, if it has the 'er' sound.

5.  Decide on the winning criteria – either a time limit, a points value, or a certain number of words.

# Er, What's the Word?

Dice

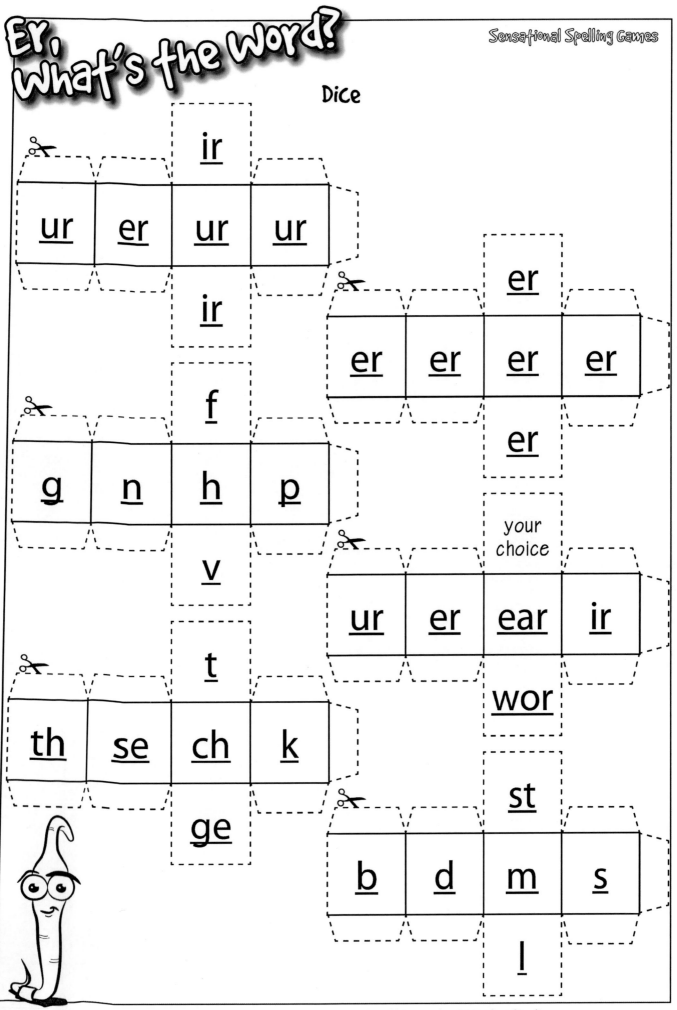

ir

| ur | er | ur | ur |

ir

| er | er | er | er |

er

er

f

| g | n | h | p |

v

your choice

| ur | er | ear | ir |

t

wor

| th | se | ch | k |

ge

st

| b | d | m | s |

l

# Er, What's the Word?

## Word List

✂

| ear | er | ir | ur | wor | +er |
|-----|-----|-----|-----|-----|-----|
| earl | berg | bird | burn | word | burner |
| earth | berm | birch | burp | work | burger |
| earn | berth | birth | burst | worm | earner |
| heard | fern | chirp | churn | worse | further |
| hearse | germ | dirt | fur | worst | firmer |
| learn | her | dirge | furl | worth | worker |
| pearl | herb | fir | hurt | | girder |
| | herd | first | hurl | | herder |
| | merge | girl | lurk | | learner |
| | per | gird | murk | | merger |
| | Perth | girth | nurse | | |
| | perm | mirth | purse | | |
| | pert | sir | purl | | |
| | perk | stir | purge | | |
| | perch | thirst | surf | | |
| | stern | third | surge | | |
| | tern | | turn | | |
| | term | | turf | | |
| | verb | | urn | | |
| | verge | | | | |
| | verse | | | | |

## Individual Score card

✂

| My Name: _____ **Words I Made** | 5pts for each word | Bonus 5pts for 2 syllables | Total for turn |
|---|---|---|---|
| | | | |
| | | | |
| | | | |
| | | | |
| | | | |
| | | | |
| | | | |
| | Total points for game: | | |

# Scare the Hairy Bears

'are' 'air' 'ear' 'eer' sounds

2–6 Players

## Preparation

Photocopy the game on to coloured card and back the word cards with the small pictures. Laminate if desired. Cut out the small cards. Sort the cards according to the pictures on the back and keep in separate piles.

## How to play (for reading practice):

1. Each player needs a playing marker.

2. Place the cards in piles in the centre of the board, picture side up.

3. The first player picks up a card which matches the first picture on the board. If they can read the words correctly **they place the card on the bottom of the pile** and move the number indicated by the stars on the bottom of the card.

4. If the player cannot read the words, the card is put on the bottom of the pile and the player does not move.

5. Continue in this way until a player has reached the centre of the board. (You may choose to have all the players reach the centre).

6. **The winner is the first player to reach the picnic.**

## How to play (for spelling practice):

1. Play in the same manner, but the teacher picks up the cards for each player and dictates the words or sentence.

2. The player moves the number indicated by the stars on the bottom of the card and collects card if the spelling is correct.

3. Continue in this way until a player has reached the centre of the board. (You may choose to have all the players reach the centre.)

4. **The winner is the one with the most cards at the end of the game.**

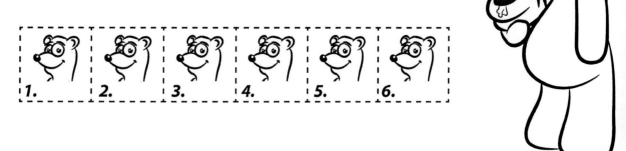

1.  2.  3.  4.  5.  6.

| | | | | |
|---|---|---|---|---|
| wear<br>swear<br>spear | steer<br>sheer<br>sneer | deer<br>fear<br>near<br>gear | engineer<br>pioneer<br>volunteer | aeroplane<br>aerial |
| sphere<br>hemisphere<br>atmosphere | year<br>yearly<br>appear<br>disappear | here<br>where<br>there | bear<br>pear<br>dear<br>fear | peer<br>beer<br>deer |
| airport<br>aircraft<br>airmail | fair<br>hair<br>pair | square<br>snare<br>glare | air<br>hair<br>chair | prepare<br>declare<br>glare |
| rare<br>scare<br>mare | aware<br>beware<br>warehouse | care<br>bare<br>dare<br>fare | pair<br>repair<br>stairs | hairy<br>fairy |
| Beware of the deer in there. | Prepare the spare tyre for repair. | The aeroplane took off from the airfield. | Repair the gear so I can steer. | Don't despair of finding the rare spear. |
| I bought a pair of chairs at the fair. | Don't tear the chair. | The bears were trapped in a snare. | How dare you glare like that! | The bear stared at the deer. |
| The aeronautical engineer started his career at the airport. | The pioneer speared deer for skins to wear. | A pair of bears ate all the pears. | Cheer the weary players. They nearly won. | Don't despair when your peers sneer at you. |

# Scare the Hairy Bears

**Bear cards**

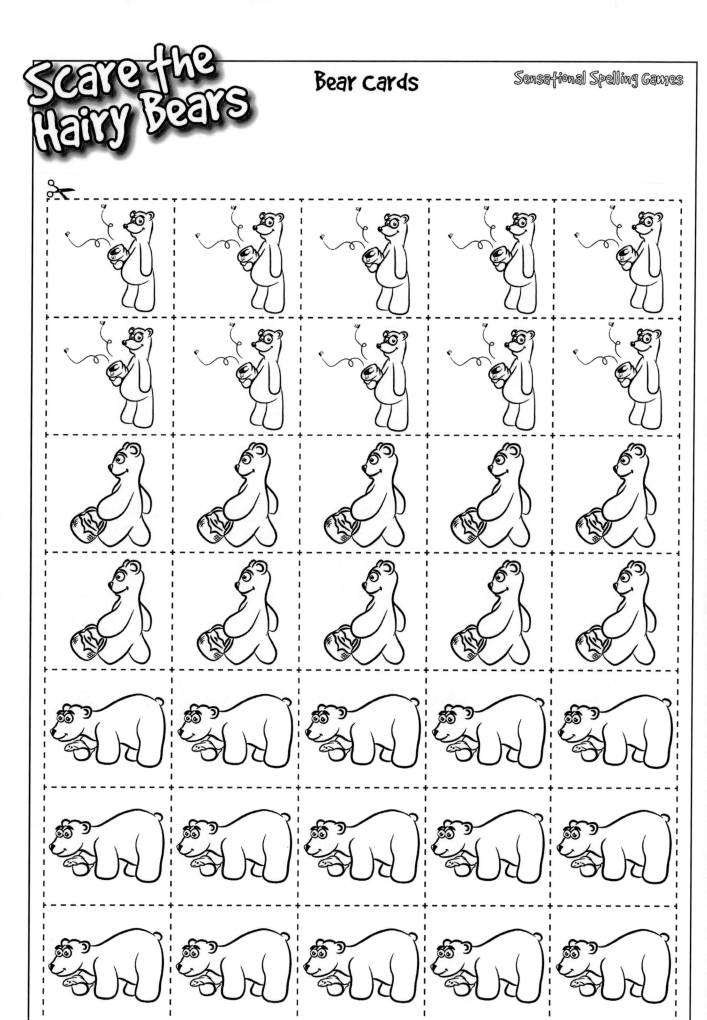

# Game Board